POEMS
OF
WORSHIP

Chosen by

IRENE O'BRIEN, B.A.

Headmistress, Eastwood County Infants' School, Nottinghamshire

BASIL BLACKWELL · OXFORD

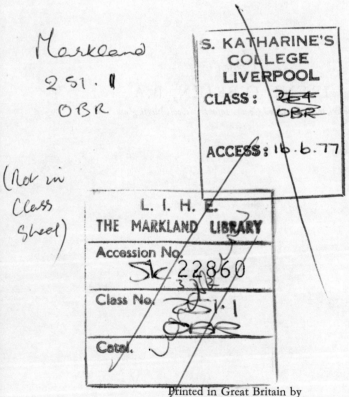
Printed in Great Britain by
William Clowes & Sons, Limited, London, Beccles and Colchester
and bound by the Kemp Hall Bindery

FOREWORD

THESE poems have proved suitable to read to infants and
lower juniors in the Act of Worship. It is hoped that teachers
will find the anthology useful too on many other occasions.

The poems are not always quoted in their entirety unless
they are wholly suitable for young children. The reader may
on occasion feel that there is need for further abbreviation.

Titles and page numbers of poems in this book are quoted
in the companion book *Themes of Worship*.

CONTENTS

God's Wonderful World

Music and Song

Birds and Beasts

Trees and Flowers

Verse:

Spring

Verses:

xi

The Lord Jesus

Verses:

School

Home

Verse:

People who work for us

I am wonderfully made

Verse:

Playtime

Verse:

SUN, MOON AND STARS

Verses

God made two great lights;
The greater light to rule the day,
And the lesser light to rule the night:
He made the stars also.
And God set them in the firmament
of heaven to give light upon the earth.

Genesis I. 16–17

Look at the stars! look, look up at the skies!
O look at all the fire-folk sitting in the air!

Gerard Manley Hopkins

Truly the light is sweet, and a
pleasant thing it is for the eyes
to behold the sun.

Ecclesiastes XI. 7

'GREAT LORD AND KING OF EARTH AND SKY AND SEA'

JESSIE POPE

Great Lord and King of Earth and Sky and Sea,
Who yet can hear a little child like me,
Who gives us everything we ask and more,
These are the things I want to thank You for—

For Brother Sun, whose bright and welcome face
Brings light and colour to each dingy place;
Who, in the golden rays he flashes down,
Reveals the shining glory of Thy crown.

For Sister Moon, whose splendour soft and white
Makes out-of-doors so beautiful at night.
For all the tiny silver stars on high,
A shower of sparkling snowflakes in the sky.

From 'St. Francis' Song of the Creatures'

I

DONNYBROOK

JAMES STEPHENS

I saw the moon, so broad and bright,
Sailing high on a frosty night!

And the air shone silverly between
The pearly queen, and the silver queen!

And here a white, and there a white
Cloud-mist swam in a mist of light!

And, all encrusted in the sky,
High, and higher, and yet more high,

Were golden star-points glimmering through
The hollow vault, the vault of blue!

And then I knew—that God was good,
And the world was fair! And, where I stood,

I bent the knee, and bent the head:
And said my prayers, and went to bed.

'THE LIGHTS FROM THE PARLOUR
AND KITCHEN'

ROBERT LOUIS STEVENSON

The lights from the parlour and kitchen shone out
Through the blinds and the windows and bars;
And high overhead and all moving about,
There were thousands of millions of stars.
There ne'er were such thousands of leaves on a tree,
Nor of people in church or the park,
As the crowds of the stars that looked down upon me,
And that glittered and winked in the dark.

From 'Escape at Bedtime'

'THE MOON SHINES CLEAR AS SILVER'

C. D. COLE

The moon shines clear as silver,
The sun shines bright as gold,
And both are very lovely
And very, very old.

From 'Sun and Moon'

'WHILE WALKING THROUGH THE TRAMS AND CARS'

JAMES STEPHENS

While walking through the trams and cars
I chanced to look up at the sky
And saw that it was full of stars!

And some were shining furiously;
And some were big and some were small;
But all were beautiful to see.

Blue stars and gold! A sky of grey!
The air between a velvet pall!
I could not take my eyes away.

From 'Blue stars and gold'

THE NIGHT SKY

ANONYMOUS

All day long
    The sun shines bright.
The moon and stars
    Come out by night.
From twilight time
    They line the skies
And watch the world
    With quiet eyes.

THE STARS

CHRISTINA ROSSETTI

What do the stars do
  Up in the sky,
Higher than the wind can blow
  Or the clouds fly?

Each star in its own glory
  Circles, circles still;
As it was lit to shine and set
  And do its Master's will.

DAY AND NIGHT

Verses

Thank God for sleep in the long quiet night,
For the clear day calling through the little leaded panes
John Drinkwater

This is the day the Lord hath made;
We will rejoice and be glad in it.
Psalm CXVIII. 24

'MATTHEW, MARK, LUKE AND JOHN'

ANONYMOUS

Matthew, Mark, Luke and John,
Bless the bed that I lie on.

NIGHT

WILLIAM BLAKE

The sun descending in the west,
The evening star does shine,
The birds are silent in their nest,
And I must seek for mine.
The moon, like a flower,
In heaven's high bower
With silent delight
Sits and smiles on the night.

DAY AND NIGHT

LADY LINDSAY

Said Day to Night,
'I bring God's light.
What gift have you?'
Night said, 'The dew'.

'I give bright hours',
Quoth Day, 'and flowers'.
Said Night, 'More blest,
I bring sweet rest'.

FATHER, WE THANK THEE

ANONYMOUS

Father, we thank Thee for the night
And for the pleasant morning light,
For rest and food and loving care,
And all that makes the world so fair.
Help us to do the things we should.
To be to others kind and good,
In all we do, in all we say,
To grow more loving every day.

'NOW THAT THE DAYLIGHT FILLS THE SKY'

J. M. NEALE

Now that the daylight fills the sky,
We lift our hearts to God on high,
That He, in all we do or say,
Would keep us free from harm today.

'WHEN, IN THE MORNING'

CECILIA LOFTUS

When in the morning, fresh from sleep,
I from my open window peep,
I always find some new surprise
To greet my grateful, wondering eyes.

From 'In the morning'

'THE MORNING BRIGHT'

THOMAS O. SUMMERS

The morning bright,
With rosy light
Has waked me up from sleep;
Father, I own,
Thy love alone,
Thy little one doth keep.

TODAY

THOMAS CARLYLE

So here hath been dawning
   Another blue day:
Think, wilt thou let it
   Slip useless away?

Out of Eternity
   This new day is born;
Into Eternity
   At night will return.

Behold it aforetime,
   No eye ever did:
So soon it forever
   From all eyes is hid.

Here hath been dawning
   Another blue day;
Think, wilt thou let it
   Slip useless away.

7

TIME TO GO HOME

JAMES REEVES

Time to go home!
  Says the great steeple clock.
Time to go home!
  Says the gold weathercock.
Down sinks the sun
  In the valley to sleep;
Lost are the orchards
  In blue shadows deep.
Soft falls the dew
  On cornfield and grass;
Through the dark trees
  The evening airs pass:
Time to go home!
  They murmur and say,
Birds to their homes
  Have all flown away.
Nothing shines now
  But the gold weathercock.
Time to go home!
  Says the great steeple clock.

8

RAIN

Verse

I will give the rain in its season,
that thou mayest gather in thy food.

Deuteronomy XI. 14

'HOW BEAUTIFUL IS THE RAIN!'

HENRY WADSWORTH LONGFELLOW

How beautiful is the rain!
After the dust and heat,
In the broad and fiery street
In the narrow lane
How beautiful is the rain!

From 'Rain in Summer'

APRIL SHOWERS

ANONYMOUS

Patter, patter, let it pour,
Patter, patter, let it roar;
Down the steep roof let it rush,
Down the hillside let it gush;
'Tis the welcome April shower,
Which will wake the sweet May flower.

'THE DROPS STILL HANG ON LEAF AND THORN'

EDWARD SHANKS

The drops still hang on leaf and thorn,
The downs stand up more green;
The sun comes out again in power,
And the sky is washed and clean.

From 'The Storm'

9

'EVERY VALLEY DRINKS'

CHRISTINA ROSSETTI
Every valley drinks,
   Every dell and hollow;
Where the kind rain sinks and sinks,
   Green of spring will follow.

From 'Winter Rain'

'I LIKE THE RAIN'

PATRICK CHALMERS
I like the rain, I like the smell
Of tired old Earth made young and well;
Grey rain, it makes the green wheat swell,
The rivers run;
And welcomer than I can tell
It makes the sun.

From 'I Like'

'THIS IS THE WEATHER
THE CUCKOO LIKES'

THOMAS HARDY
This is the weather the cuckoo likes,
   And so do I;
When showers betumble the chestnut spikes,
   And nestlings fly.
And the little brown nightingale bills his best,
And they sit outside at 'The Travellers' Rest',
And maids come forth sprig-muslin drest,
And citizens dream of the south and west,
   And so do I.

From 'Weathers'

WATER

NANCY BYRD TURNER

Water is a lovely thing:
Dark and ripply in a spring;
Black and quiet in a pool,
In a puddle brown and cool;
In a river blue and gay,
In a raindrop silver-grey;
In a fountain flashing white,
In a dewdrop crystal bright;
In a pitcher frosty-cold,
In a bubble pink and gold,
In a happy summer sea
Just as green as green can be;
In a rainbow, far unfurled,
Every colour in the world,
All the year, from spring to spring,
Water is the loveliest thing!

GOD'S WONDERFUL WORLD

Verses

And God saw everything that he had
made, and, behold, it was very good.

Genesis I. 31

By him were all things created,
that are in heaven, and that
are in earth.

Colossians I. 16

'LOOK FOR A LOVELY THING'

SARA TEASDALE

Look for a lovely thing and
you will find it,
It is not far—
It never will be far.

From 'Night'

'THOU WHO HAST GIVEN SO MUCH'

GEORGE HERBERT

Thou, who hast given so much to me,
Give one thing more, a grateful heart.

From 'A grateful heart'

'SKY SO BRIGHT'

ANONYMOUS

Sky so bright
Blue and light,
Stars how many hast thou?
 Countless stars.
Countless times
Shall our God be praised now.

Forest green,
Cool, serene,
Leaves how many hast thou?
 Countless leaves.
Countless times
Shall our God be praised now.

Deepest sea,
Wide and free,
Waves how many hast thou?
 Countless waves.
Countless times
Shall our God be praised now.

   From 'A Song in Praise of the Lord'

WHAT IS PINK?

CHRISTINA ROSSETTI

What is pink?
  A rose is pink
By the fountain's brink.

What is red?
  A poppy's red
In its barley bed.

What is blue?
  The sky is blue
Where the clouds float through.

What is white?
            A swan is white
Sailing in the light.

What is yellow?
            Pears are yellow.
Rich and ripe and mellow.

What is green?
            The grass is green
With small flowers between.

What is violet?
            Clouds are violet
In the summer twilight.

What is orange?
            Why, an orange,
Just an orange!

'I LOVE ALL SHINING THINGS'

ELIZABETH GOULD

I love all shining things—
            the lovely moon,
The silver stars at night,
            gold sun at noon.
A glowing rainbow in
            a stormy sky,
Or bright clouds hurrying
            when wind goes by.

From 'Shining Things'

'FOR JOY OF GLOWING COLOUR'

ELIZABETH GOULD

For joy of glowing colour, flash of wings,
We thank Thee, Lord; for all the little things
That make the love and laughter of our days,
For home and happiness and friends, we praise
            And thank Thee now.

From 'Grace and Thanksgiving'

'GOD GIVES SO MANY LOVELY THINGS!'

NANCY BYRD TURNER

God gives so many lovely things!
He gives the bird its feathery wings,
The butterfly its colours fair,
The bee a velvet coat to wear.

He gives the garden all its flowers,
And sun to make them grow, and showers,
Red apples for the old bent tree,
Wheat in the meadow blowing free.

Cool grass upon the summer hills,
And silvery streams to turn the mills.
He gives the shining day, and then
The quiet, starry night again.

From 'God's Providence'

'WE THANK THEE, LORD, FOR THIS FAIR EARTH'

BISHOP GEORGE COTTON

We thank Thee, Lord, for this fair earth,
The glittering sky, the silver sea;
For all their beauty, all their worth,
Their light and glory, come from Thee.

'WE THANK YOU, LORD OF HEAVEN'

JAN STRUTHER

We thank You, Lord of Heaven,
    For all the joys that greet us,
For all that You have given
    To help us and delight us
        In earth and sky and seas;
The sunlight on the meadows,
    The rainbow's fleeting wonder,
The clouds with cooling shadows,
    The stars that shine in splendour—
        We thank You, Lord, for these.

'TO GOD, WHO MAKES ALL LOVELY THINGS'

REV. J. M. CRUM

To God, Who makes all lovely things,
How happy must our praises be.
Each day a new surprise He brings
To make us glad His world to see.

'THE WORLD'S A VERY HAPPY PLACE'

GABRIEL SETOUN

The world's a very happy place,
Where every child should dance and sing,
And always have a smiling face,
And never sulk for anything.
From 'The World's Music'

'GIVE ME A SENSE OF HUMOUR, LORD'

ANONYMOUS

Give me a sense of humour, Lord,
Give me the grace to see a joke,
To get some happiness from life,
And pass it on to other folk.
From 'Give me a good digestion, Lord'

'COME, LET US REMEMBER THE JOYS OF THE TOWN'

DORIS M. GILL

Come, let us remember the joys of the town:
Gay vans and bright buses that roar up and down,
Shop windows and playgrounds and swings in the park,
And street-lamps that twinkle in rows after dark.

MUSIC AND SONG

Verse

I will sing unto the Lord as long as I live.

Psalm CIV. 33

GOLDENHAIR

JAMES JOYCE

Lean out of the window
  Goldenhair,
I heard you singing
  A merry air.

My book is closed;
  I read no more,
Watching the fire dance
  On the floor.

I have left my book;
  I have left my room,
For I heard you singing
  Through the gloom.

Singing and singing
  A merry air,
Lean out of the window,
  Goldenhair.

A PIPER

SEUMAS O'SULLIVAN

A piper in the streets today
Set up and tuned, and started to play,
And away, away, away on the tide
Of his music we started; on every side
Doors and windows were opened wide,
And men left down their work and came,
And women with petticoats coloured like flame,
And little bare feet that were blue with cold,
Went dancing back to the age of gold,
And all the world went gay, went gay,
For half an hour in the street today.

ANSWER TO A CHILD'S QUESTION

SAMUEL TAYLOR COLERIDGE

Do you know what the birds say? The Sparrow, the Dove,
The Linnet and Thrush say, 'I love and I love!'
In the winter they're silent—the wind is so strong;
What it says, I don't know, but it sings a loud song.

But green leaves, and blossoms, and sunny warm weather,
And singing, and loving—all come back together.
And the lark is so brimful of gladness and love,
The green fields below him, the blue sky above,
That he sings, and he sings and for ever sings he—
'I love my Love and my Love loves me!'

BIRDS AND BEASTS

Verses

By him were all things created.

Colossians 1. 16

I think I could turn and live
with animals.

Walt Whitman

O little lark, sing loud and long
To him who gave you flight and song.

Anna Bunston

MICHAEL'S SONG

WILFRED GIBSON

Because I set no snare
    But leave them flying free,
All the birds of the air
    Belong to me.

From the blue-tit on the sloe
    To the eagle on the height,
Uncaged they come and go
    For my delight.

And so the sunward way
    I soar on the eagle's wings,
And in my heart all day
    The blue-tit sings.

FULL EARLY IN THE MORNING

ANONYMOUS

Full early in the morning
    Awakes the summer sun,

19

The month of June arriving,
　　The cold and night are done;
The cuckoo is a fine bird,
　　She whistles as she flies,
And as she whistles 'cuckoo',
　　The bluer grow the skies.

'GOOD-BYE, GOOD-BYE TO SUMMER'

WILLIAM ALLINGHAM

Good-bye, good-bye to Summer!
　　For Summer's nearly done;
The garden smiling faintly
　　Cool breezes in the sun;
Our Thrushes now are silent,
　　Our Swallows flown away,
But Robin's here, in coat of brown,
And ruddy breast-knot gay.
　　Robin, Robin Redbreast,
　　　　O Robin dear!
　　Robin singing sweetly
　　　　In the falling of the year.

From 'Robin Redbreast'

WELCOME, LITTLE ROBIN

ANONYMOUS

Welcome, little Robin,
　　With your scarlet breast,
In this winter weather
　　Cold must be your nest.
Hopping on the carpet,
　　Picking up the crumbs,
Robin knows the children
　　Love him when he comes.

THE BLACKBIRD

In the far corner,
close by the swings,
every morning
a blackbird sings.

His bill's so yellow,
his coat's so black,
that he makes a fellow
whistle back.

CUCKOO

ANONYMOUS

Cuckoo, Cuckoo,
What do you do?

In April
I open my bill.

In May
I sing night and day.

In June
I change my tune.

In July
Up high I fly.

In August
Away I must.

'HE COMES ON CHOSEN EVENINGS'

JOHN DRINKWATER

He comes on chosen evenings,
My blackbird bountiful, and sings
Over the gardens of the town
Just at the hour the sun goes down.

From 'Blackbird'

21

SPARROW

LEONARD CLARK

You seem to be always there
Chirping the whole year through
In country lane, city square
With gossip enough for two.

You really are a speck
Of mischief when in showers
I watch you greedily peck
At the yellow crocus flowers.

Brown, pin-eyed, small
You follow me around,
Nest in a hole in a wall,
Speckle the air with sound.

On dusty matchstick feet
Hop away into the sun,
Play in the rainy street,
You little rapscallion.

THE BLACKBIRD

PHYLLIS DRAYSON

Out in the garden,
    Up in a tree,
There is a blackbird
    Singing to me.

What is he singing
    Up in the tree?
What is he piping
    So merrily?

Come out in the garden,
  Come out and hear!
Stand still and listen
  (But not too near).

I love the wind and the stars and the moon,
I love the sun when it shines at noon;
I love the trees, but I love best
My little brown wife in our cosy nest!

That is the song
  He's singing to me,
That's what he's piping
  So merrily!

'A ROBIN REDBREAST IN A CAGE'

WILLIAM BLAKE

A robin redbreast in a cage
Puts all Heaven in a rage . . .
He who shall hurt the little wren
Shall never be belov'd by men.
From 'Auguries of Innocence'

'TO ALL THE HUMBLE BEASTS THERE BE'

JOHN GALSWORTHY

To all the humble beasts there be,
To all the birds on land and sea,
Great Spirit! sweet protection give,
That free and happy they may live!
From 'Prayer for gentleness to all creatures'

TO A SQUIRREL

Come play with me;
Why should you run
Through the shaking tree
As though I'd a gun?
When all I would do
Is to scratch your head
And let you go.

'FOR SWIFT AND GALLANT HORSES'

For swift and gallant horses,
  For lambs in pastures springing,
For dogs with friendly faces,
  For birds with music thronging
  Their chantries in the trees;
For herbs to cool our fever,
  For flowers of field and garden,
For bees among the clover
  With stolen sweetness laden—
  We thank you, Lord, for these.
              From 'We thank you, Lord of Heaven'

'LITTLE LAMB, WHO MADE THEE?'

Little lamb, who made thee?
Dost thou know who made thee,
Gave thee life, and bade thee feed
By the streams and o'er the mead;
Gave thee clothing of delight,
Softest clothing, woolly, bright;
Gave thee such a tender voice
Making all the vales rejoice?
  Little lamb, who made thee?
  Dost thou know who made thee?
              From 'The Lamb'

MY DOG, SPOT

RODNEY BENNETT

I have a white dog
  Whose name is Spot,
And he's sometimes white
  And he's sometimes not.
But whether he's white
  Or whether he's not,
There's a patch on his ear
  That makes him Spot.

He has a tongue
  That is long and pink
And he lolls it out
  When he wants to think,
He seems to think most
  When the weather is hot.
He's a wise sort of dog,
  Is my dog, Spot.

He likes a bone
  And he likes a ball,
But he doesn't care
  For a cat at all.
He waggles his tail
  And he knows what's what,
So I'm glad that he's my dog,
  My dog, Spot.

TREES AND FLOWERS

Verse

Every good gift and every
perfect gift is from above.

St. James I. 17

TREES

SARA COLERIDGE

The Oak is called the King of Trees,
The Aspen quivers in the breeze,
The Poplar grows up straight and tall,
The Pear tree spreads along the wall,
The Sycamore gives pleasant shade,
The Willow droops in watery glade,
The Fir tree useful timber gives,
The Beech amid the forest lives.

'LOVELIEST OF TREES, THE CHERRY NOW'

A. E. HOUSMAN

Loveliest of trees, the cherry now
Is hung with bloom along the bough,
And stands about the woodland ride
Wearing white for Easter-tide.

'THERE'S A TREE OUT IN OUR GARDEN'

CHRISTINE CHAUNDLER

There's a tree out in our garden which is very nice to climb,
And I often go and climb it when it's fine in summer time,
And when I've climbed right up it I pretend it's not a tree
But a ship in which I'm sailing far away across the sea.

From 'The Tree in the Garden'

26

THE BEECH TREE

ROSE FYLEMAN

I'd like to have a garden
  With a beech-tree on the lawn;
The little birds that lived there
  Would wake me up at dawn.

And in the summer weather
  When all the leaves were green,
I'd sit beneath the beech-boughs
  And see the sky between.

'THERE IS A FLOWER'

JAMES MONTGOMERY

There is a flower, a little flower,
With silver crest and golden eye
That welcomes every changing hour
And weathers every sky.

From 'The Daisy'

'DO YOU LIKE MARIGOLDS?'

LOUISE DRISCOLL

Do you like marigolds?
  If you do
Then my garden is
  Gay for you!

I've been cutting their
  Fragrant stalks
Where they lean on
  The garden walks.

From 'Marigolds'

'IN THE BLUEBELL FOREST'

O. ENOCH

In the bluebell forest
There is scarce a sound
Only bluebells growing
Everywhere around.

I can't see a blackbird
Or a thrush to sing,
I think I can almost
Here the bluebells ring.

From 'Bluebells'

'BUTTERCUPS AND DAISIES'

MARY HOWITT

Buttercups and daisies,
Oh, the pretty flowers,
Coming e'er the spring-time
To tell of sunny hours,
While the trees are leafless,
While the fields are bare,
Buttercups and daisies
Spring up here and there.

THE DANDELION

FRANCES CORNFORD

The dandelion is brave and gay,
And loves to grow beside the way;
A braver thing was never seen,
To praise the grass for growing green.
You never saw a gayer thing
To sit and smile and praise the spring.

'HERE ARE SWEET PEAS'

JOHN KEATS

Here are sweet peas, on tiptoe for a flight:
With wings of gentle flush o'er delicate white.

From 'Sweet Peas'

ROSES

GEORGE ELIOT

You love the roses—so do I. I wish
The sky would rain down roses, as they rain
From off the shaken bush. Why will it not?
Then all the valley would be pink and white
And soft to tread on. They would fall as light
As feathers, smelling sweet: and it would be
Like sleeping and yet waking, all at once.

POPPIES

P. A. ROPES

The strange, bright dancers
Are in the garden.
The wind of Summer
Is a soft music.
Scarlet and orange,
Flaming and golden,
The strange, bright dancers
Move to the music.
And some are whiter
Than snow in winter,
And float like snowflakes
Drifting the garden.
Oh, have you seen them
The strange, bright dancers,
Nodding and swaying
To the wind's music?

WINDOW-BOXES

ELEANOR FARJEON

A window-box of pansies
Is such a happy thing.
A window-box of wallflowers
Is a garden for a king.

A window-box of roses
Makes everyone stand still
Who sees a garden growing
On a window-sill.

'WARM IN THE BLANKETS OF THE EARTH'

B. R. GIBBS

Warm in the blankets of the earth you lay,
    But you have dared to thrust aside the night
And tilt your chalk-soft spear against the day,
    While still his armour glitters, winter-white;
Yet, foolish snowdrop, for the hope you bring
These eyes have never seen a lovelier thing.

From 'First Snowdrop'

'LITTLE LADIES, WHITE AND GREEN'

L. ALMA TADEMA

Little ladies, white and green,
    With your spears about you,
Will you tell us where you've been
    Since we lived without you?

Little ladies, white and green,
    Are you glad to cheer us?
Hunger not for where you've been,
    Stay till Spring be near us!

From 'Snowdrops'

'THE GARDEN FLOWERS INSIDE THE WALL'

ELEANOR FARJEON

The garden flowers inside the wall
Belong to him who planted them,
But God once sowed the wildflowers all
For anyone who wanted them.

From 'Wildflowers'

'JUST NOW THE LILAC IS IN BLOOM'

RUPERT BROOKE

Just now the lilac is in bloom
All before my little room
And in my garden beds, I think,
Smile the carnation and the pink.

From 'The Old Vicarage, Grantchester'

SOWING SEEDS

URSULA CORNWALL

I've dug up all my garden
And got the watering can,
And packets full of seeds I mean to sow;
I'll have marigolds and pansies,
And Canterbury bells,
And asters all set neatly in a row.
I'll have mignonette and stocks,
And some tall red hollyhocks,
If sun and rain will come to help them grow.

SPRING

Verses

For, lo, the winter is past,
The rain is over and gone;
The flowers appear on the earth;
The time of the singing of birds is come.

Song of Solomon II. 11, 12

All happy and glad in the sunshine I stood,
For isn't Spring lovely and isn't God good?

Daniel A. Lord

Spring, the sweet Spring, is the year's pleasant king.

Thomas Nash

PROMISE

FLORENCE LACEY

There's a black fog hiding London
And every tree looks dead,
But I've seen a purple crocus and a jonquil's golden head.
The shallow ponds are frozen
And there's snow upon the hills,
But they're selling scarlet tulips now and yellow daffodils.

A bitter wind is blowing,
The rivers are abrim,
But I toss my head at Winter, I am not afraid of him.
Although the sun is shrouded
Spring is just across the sea,
For I've seen a spray of lilac and a red anemone.

'LOOK! LOOK! THE SPRING IS COME'

ROBERT BRIDGES

Look! Look! the Spring is come:
O feel the gentle air,
That wanders through the boughs to burst
The thick buds everywhere!
The birds are glad to see
The high unclouded sun:
Winter is fled away, they sing,
The gay time is begun.

From 'First Spring Morning'

WINTER AND SPRING

ANONYMOUS

But a little while ago
All the ground was white with snow;
Trees and shrubs were dry and bare,
Not a sign of life was there;
Now the buds and leaves are seen
Now the fields are fresh and green,
Pretty birds are on the wing,
With a merry song they sing!
There's new life in everything!
How I love the pleasant Spring!

WELCOME TO SPRING

IRENE THOMPSON

I have heard a mother bird
   Singing in the rain—
Telling all her little ones
   Spring has come again!

I have seen a wave of green
   Down a lovely lane—
Making all the hedges glad
   Spring has come again!

33

I have found a patch of ground
  Golden in the sun;
Crocuses are calling out
  Spring has just begun.

PIPPA'S SONG

ROBERT BROWNING

The year's at the spring,
The day's at the morn;
Morning's at seven;
The hill-side's dew-pearled;
The lark's on the wing;
The snail's on the thorn;
God's in His heaven—
All's right in the world.

MERRY BIRDS

RODNEY BENNETT

Merrily, merrily,
All the Spring,
Merrily, merrily,
Small birds sing.
All through April,
All through May,
Small birds merrily
Carol all day.

THANKS TO SPRING

MARY ANDERSON

We thank Thee, Heavenly Father,
  For all the lovely Spring,
For primroses and bluebells
  And little birds that sing.

For woods and fields to play in,
  For bright blue sky and sea,
For everything we thank Thee
  All beauty comes from Thee.

SPRING PRAYER

RALPH WALDO EMERSON

For flowers that bloom about our feet;
For tender grass, so fresh, so sweet;
For song of bird, and hum of bee;
For all things fair we hear or see,
Father in heaven, we thank Thee!

For blue of stream and blue of sky;
For pleasant shade of branches high;
For fragrant air and cooling breeze;
For beauty of the blooming trees;
Father in heaven, we thank Thee!

'THE SUN DOES ARISE'

WILLIAM BLAKE

The Sun does arise
And make happy the skies;
The merry bells ring
To welcome the Spring.
From 'The Echoing Green'

MY GARDEN BED IS READY

My garden bed is ready
  For little sleeping seeds,
I've dug and raked and watered
  And pulled up all the weeds.
When God has sent the sunshine
  And raindrops day by day
The little seeds will waken
  And make my garden gay.
Source unknown

SUMMER

Verses

Again the Summer comes and all is fair.
                              Philip Bourke Marston

        Summer days for me
        When every leaf is on its tree
                              Christina Rossetti

    Good-bye to the Town!—good-bye!
    Hurrah! for the sea and the sky!
                              Austin Dobson

        We are getting to the short night,
            And 'summer time' is near;
        And now, within a fortnight,
            The cuckoo may be here.
                              Laurence Housman

SUMMER IS NIGH

ANONYMOUS

Summer is nigh!
How do I know?
Why, this very day
A robin sat
On a tilting spray,
And merrily sang
A song of May.
Jack Frost has fled
From the rippling brook;
And a trout peeped out
From his shady nook.
A butterfly too
Flew lazily by,
And the willow catkins
Shook from on high

36

Their yellow dust
As I passed by:
And so I know
That summer is nigh.

JUNE

IRENE F. PAWSEY

Month of leaves,
Month of roses;
Gardens full
Of dainty posies;
  Skies of blue,
  Hedgerows gay,
  Meadows sweet
  With the new-mown hay.

Flowery banks,
A-drone with bees,
Dreaming cattle
Under trees:
  Song-birds pipe
  A merry tune—
  This is Summer,
  This is June.

THE SEA

E. M. ADAMS

Take your bucket, and take your spade,
  And come to the sea with me,
Building castles upon the sand
  Is the game for you and me!
Races run with the tumbling waves,
Then rest awhile in the cool, dark caves.
Oh, the greatest joy in the summer time
  Is the sea, the sparkling sea!

THE CLIFF-TOP

ROBERT BRIDGES

The cliff-top has a carpet
    Of lilac, gold and green:
The blue sky bounds the ocean,
    The white clouds scud between.

A flock of gulls are wheeling
    And wailing round my seat;
Above my head the heaven,
    The sea beneath my feet.

THERE ARE BIG WAVES

ELEANOR FARJEON

There are big waves and little waves,
    Green waves and blue,
Waves you can jump over,
    Waves you dive thro',
Waves that rise up
    Like a great water wall,
Waves that swell softly
    And don't break at all,
Waves that can whisper,
    Waves that can roar,
And tiny waves that run at you
    Running on the shore.

AUTUMN

Verse

He made everything beautiful in his time.

Ecclesiastes III. 11

'THE WORLD IS FULL OF COLOUR'

ADELINE WHITE

The world is full of colour!
'Tis Autumn once again
And leaves of gold and crimson
Are lying in the lane.

From 'Colour'

GOLDEN, YELLOW, BROWN AND RED

E. H. RAY

Golden, yellow, brown and red,
Pirouetting overhead.
See them flutter, twist and curl
Dancing in a windblown whirl.

From 'Leaf-fall'

AN AUTUMN MORNING

ANONYMOUS

It seems like a dream
    In the garden today;
The trees, once so green,
    With rich colours are gay.

39

The oak is aglow
    With a warm crimson blush;
The maple leaves show
    A deep purple flush.

The elm tree with bold
    Yellow patches is bright,
And with pale gleaming gold
    The beech seems alight.

And the creeper leaves flare
    Like red flame on the wall;
Their dazzle and glare
    Is the brightest of all.

The big chestnut trees
    Are all russet and brown,
And everywhere leaves
    One by one flutter down.

And all the leaves seem
    To be dressed up so gay,
That it seems like a dream
    In the garden today.

'IN AUTUMN DOWN THE BEECHWOOD PATH'

JAMES REEVES

In Autumn down the beechwood path
The leaves lie thick upon the ground.
It's there I love to kick my way
And hear their crisp and crashing sound.

From 'Beech Leaves'

'THE CLOUDS MOVE FAST'

W. B. RANDS

The clouds move fast, the south is blowing,
The sun is slanting, the year is going;
O I love to walk where the leaves lie dead,
And hear them rustle beneath my tread.

From 'Autumn Song'

WIND AND THE LEAVES

ANONYMOUS

'Come, little leaves', said the wind one day,
'Come o'er the meadows with me and play;
Put on your dresses of red and gold,
For Summer is gone and the days grow cold'.

Soon as the leaves heard the wind's loud call,
Down they came fluttering, one and all;
Over the fields they danced and flew,
Singing the soft little songs they knew.

Dancing and whirling the little leaves went;
Winter had called them and they were content.
Soon, fast asleep in their earthy beds,
The snow laid a coverlet over their heads.

AUTUMN

ANONYMOUS

There are nuts on the trees
    In their clusters of brown,
And the leaves are like butterflies
    Fluttering down.

The cornfields are golden,
    The sunlight is clear,
And the apples are rosy
    Now Autumn is here.

41

MR. SQUIRREL

V. M. JULIAN

I saw a brown squirrel today in the wood,
He ran here and there just as fast as he could;
I think he was looking for nuts for his store
He'd found quite a lot, but he still wanted more.

He can't find much food once the winter is here,
He hides all his nuts in a hole somewhere near,
Then settles himself for a long winter sleep,
Coming out now and then for a nut and a peep.

His long bushy tail keeps him cosy and warm
His nest's far away from the wind and the storm.
But when Springtime comes back, I think that, maybe,
He'll be waiting again in the woodland for me.

DORMOUSE

LILIAN MCCREA

'Now Winter is coming',
The dormouse said,
'I must be thinking
Of going to bed'.
So he curled himself up
As small as he could,
And went fast asleep
As a dormouse should.

PLUMP HOUSEKEEPER DORMOUSE

J. M. MACDOUGALL FERGUSON

Plump housekeeper dormouse has tucked himself neat,
Just a brown ball in moss with a morsel to eat:
Armed hedgehog has huddled him into the hedge,
While frogs scarce miss freezing deep down in the sedge.

'THERE ARE FLOWERS ENOUGH IN THE SUMMERTIME'

MARY HOWITT

There are flowers enough in the summer-time,
   More flowers than I can remember—
But none with the purple, gold, and red
   That dye the flowers of September!
   The gorgeous flowers of September!
      And the sun looks through
      A clearer blue,
      And the moon at night
      Sheds a clearer light
On the beautiful flowers of September!

From 'September'

'THE LEAVES HAD A WONDERFUL FROLIC'

ANONYMOUS

The leaves had a wonderful frolic,
   They danced to the wind's loud song,
They whirled, and they floated, and scampered,
   They circled and flew along.

The North Wind is calling, is calling,
   And we must whirl round and round,
And then when our dancing is ended
   We'll make a warm quilt for the ground.

From 'The Leaves'

'THE SWALLOWS ARE FLYING ACROSS THE SEA'

The swallows are flying across the sea,
   Going to countries warm,
Away from the cold wind, the rain and the fog,
   Safe from the winter's storm.

Source unknown

'THE SWALLOWS ARE GONE'

The swallows are gone, I saw them gather,
I heard them murmuring of the weather.

From 'Autumn Song'

WINTER

Verses

On the wind of January
Down flits the snow,
Travelling from the frozen north
As cold as it can blow.

Anonymous

I shall smile when wreaths of snow
Blossom where the rose should grow.

Emily Brontë

I heard the snowflakes whisper in the still, dark night,
And when I peeped at bedtime all the roofs were white.

R. M. Arthur

—God knows best
The way to put all weary things to rest.

Jack Gilbey

'GET YOU OUT YOUR MUFFLER GREY'

JAMES STEPHENS

Get you out
Your muffler grey
Your boots so stout
And your great-coat, pray
And put on your gloves,
'Tis a hardy day.

From 'This way to winter'

'NOTHING IS SO QUIET AND CLEAN'

RICKMAN MARK

Nothing is so quiet and clean
As snow that falls in the night;
And isn't it jolly to jump from bed
And find the whole world white?

From 'Snow in Town'

'AS SOFT AS FEATHERS'

HILDA I. ROSTRON

As soft as feathers,
    As quiet as can be,
Something is falling
    So silently.

From 'So Silently'

THE SNOW

F. A. ELLIOTT

The snow, in bitter cold,
    Fell all the night;
And we awoke to see
    The garden white.

And still the silvery flakes
    Go whirling by,
White feathers fluttering
    From a grey sky.

46

WHITE FIELDS

JAMES STEPHENS

I

In the winter time we go
Walking in the fields of snow;

Where there is no grass at all;
Where the top of every wall,

Every fence, and every tree,
Is as white as white could be.

II

Pointing out the way we came,
—Every one of them the same—

All across the fields there be
Prints in silver filigree;

And our mothers always know,
By the footprints in the snow,

Where it is the children go.

'THE NORTH WIND DOTH BLOW'

ANONYMOUS

The north wind doth blow,
And we shall have snow,
And what will poor robin do then, poor thing?
O, he'll go to the barn,
And to keep himself warm
He'll hide his head under his wing, poor thing, . . .

The north wind doth blow,
And we shall have snow,
And what will the children do then, poor things?
O, when lessons are done,
They'll jump, skip, and run,
And play till they make themselves warm, poor things.

From 'The North Wind'

'COME IN THE GARDEN'

E. M. ADAMS

Come in the garden
And play in the snow,
A snowman we'll make,
See how quickly he'll grow.

From 'The Snowman'

MY NEW YEAR'S WISH SHALL BE

EDMUND GOSSE

My New Year's wish shall be
　For love and love alone;
More hands to hold out joy for me
　More hearts for me to own;
　For more than gold a thousandfold
　Is love that's neither bought nor sold.

EASTER

Verse

Lo, I am with you always,
even unto the end of the world.

St. Matthew XXVIII. 20

'THE WORLD ITSELF KEEPS EASTER DAY'

ANONYMOUS

The world itself keeps Easter Day,
And Easter larks are singing;
And Easter flowers are blooming gay,
And Easter buds are springing:
Alleluya, Alleluya.
The Lord of all things lives anew,
And all His works are rising too.

'JESUS LIVES, THE BELLS ARE RINGING'

LILIAN MCCREA

'Jesus lives!' the bells are ringing,
And the children gladly singing,
Smile with joy to greet Him.

Jesus lives! The world rejoices!
Praise Him, then, lift up your voices,
Jesus lives! O Jesus lives!

HARVEST

Verses

While the earth remaineth,
Seedtime and harvest,
And cold and heat,
And summer and winter,
And day and night shall not cease.

Genesis VIII. 22

All things living He doth feed,
His full hand supplies their need.

From 'Let us with a gladsome mind'
Songs of Praise, no. 12

And ye shall eat in plenty,
and be satisfied.

Joel II. 26

FESTIVAL

IRENE THOMPSON

At harvest time the earth is rich,
With fruits and colours gay,
The harvest fields are amber gold,
And trees in beauty sway.

Tall silken poppies flash bright flags
Of scarlet everywhere,
And swallows in their farewell joy,
Fly swiftly through the air.

Shy squirrels hurry through the trees
Their treasured food to hide,
And corn, full ripened by the sun,
In golden sheaves is tied.

O harvest time's a festival,
When earth's aglow with praise,
For gifts of leaf and flower and fruit,
And happy Autumn days.

'THE FRUIT HANGS RIPE'

ELEANOR FARJEON

The fruit hangs ripe, the fruit hangs sweet,
High and low in my Orchard Street,
Apples and pears, cherries and plums,
Something for everyone who comes.

From 'Orchard Street'

'SEE! THE WIDE CORNFIELDS'

LUCY DIAMOND

See! The wide cornfields are shining like gold:
Heavy the ears with the grain that they hold.
Cut them, O reapers, this bright autumn day,
Bind them and carry, and stow them away.

From 'A Rhyme of Harvest'

'APPLES ON THE APPLE TREES'

ENID BLYTON

Apples on the apple trees, brown and red and yellow,
Apples on the grass below, juicy, sweet, and mellow.

From 'Apple Song'

'SEEDS THAT TWIST AND SEEDS THAT TWIRL'

HILDA I. ROSTRON

Seeds that twist and seeds that twirl,
Seeds with wings which spin and whirl;

Seeds that float on thistle-down,
Seeds in coats of glossy brown; . . .

Seeds of every shape and size,
Soon will sleep 'neath winter skies.

From 'Seeds'

'BREAD IS A LOVELY THING TO EAT'

H. M. SARSON

Bread is a lovely thing to eat—
God bless the barley and the wheat!

From 'Lovely Things'

'HARVEST TIME IS HERE AGAIN'

D. M. PRESTCOTT

Harvest time is here again,
Farmers cut the golden grain; . . .
God has given us winter food.
Let us thank Him; He is good.

From 'Harvest Time'

'O DOWN IN THE ORCHARD'

HELEN LEUTY

O down in the orchard
'Tis harvesting time,
And up the tall ladders
The fruit pickers climb.

Among the green branches
That sway overhead
The apples are hanging
All rosy and red.

From 'Apple Harvest'

ROBIN SANG SWEETLY

ANONYMOUS

Robin sang sweetly
In the Autumn days,
'There are fruits for everyone.
Let all give praise!'

WE THANK THEE FOR THY LOVING GIFTS

J. M. MACDOUGALL FERGUSON

We thank Thee for Thy loving gifts
 Of sunshine warm and show'rs of rain
That ripened all the lovely fruits
 And fields of golden grain.

O, give us loving, thankful hearts
 For all Thy goodness, love and care,
And help us always to be glad
 To give away and share.

CHRISTMAS

Verses

For God so loved the world, that He gave his
only begotten Son.

St. John III. 16

Unto you is born this day in the city of David a Saviour,
Who is Christ the Lord.

St. Luke II. 11

She brought forth her firstborn son,
and she wrapped Him in swaddling clothes
and laid Him in a manger; because there
was no room for them in the inn.

St. Luke II. 7

As Joseph was a-walking,
He heard an angel sing:
'This night there shall be born
On earth our heavenly king'.

From 'The Cherry Tree Carol'

'WINDS THROUGH THE OLIVE TREES'

ANONYMOUS

Winds through the olive trees softly did blow
Round little Bethlehem long, long ago.
Sheep on the hillsides lay white as the snow;
Shepherds were watching them long, long ago.

From 'A Christmas Song'

CHRISTMAS

MARY I. OSBORN

An azure sky,
All star-bestrewn.
A lowly crib,
A hushèd room.
An open door,
A hill afar
Where little lambs
And shepherds are.
To such a world,
On such a night,
Came Jesus—
Little Lord of Light.

LIGHT THE CANDLES ON THE TREE

J. M. MACDOUGALL FERGUSON

Light the candles on the tree,
   Christ was born for you and me;
Light the candles in the hall,
   He was born to help us all;
Light the candles up and down,
   In the country and the town.
Light the candles everywhere,
   He was born a Baby fair.

'ONCE A LITTLE BABE WAS BORN'

J. M. MACDOUGALL FERGUSON

Once a little Babe was born,
   Long years ago,
Shepherds came, in light of morn,
   Bowing heads low!
Wise men brought their gifts with love,
   Reverence and fear!
God had sent from Heaven above
   His Son most dear!

         From 'Once a gentle little ass'

'I SING OF A MAID'

ANONYMOUS

I sing of a maid that is matchless
King of all Kings to her son she chose.

He came all so still where his mother was,
As dew in April that falleth on the grass.

He came all so still to his mother's bower,
As dew in April that falleth on the flower.

He came all so still where his mother lay,
As dew in April that falleth on the spray.

Mother and maiden was never none but she,
Well may such a Lady God's mother be.

A CHRISTMAS VERSE

'KAY'

He had no royal palace,
   Only a stable bare.
He had no watchful servants,
   An ox and ass stood there.
But light shone forth from where He lay;
The King of Love upon the hay!

'CHILD TIME, GLAD TIME'

WILLIS BOYD ALLEN

Child time, glad time,
   The world is young again;
The starlight streams, the holly gleams
   Upon the frosted pane;
Grant us, dear Lord, a place beside
The baby Christ, at Christmastide.
                     From 'Christmastide

'OVER THE DESERT'

NANCY M. BETTESWORTH

Over the desert
From lands far away,
We have been riding
By night and by day.
Our camels move swiftly,
Their harness bells ring;
A star shines above us
To show us a King.

From 'The Song of the Wise Men'

SONG

EUGENE FIELD

Why do the bells of Christmas ring?
Why do little children sing?

Once a lovely shining star,
Seen by shepherds from afar,
Gently moved until its light
Made a manger's cradle bright.
There a darling baby lay
Pillowed soft upon the hay;
And its mother sung and smiled:
'This is Christ, the holy Child!'

Therefore bells for Christmas ring,
Therefore little children sing.

'WHAT CAN I GIVE HIM?'

CHRISTINA ROSSETTI

What can I give Him
Poor as I am?
If I were a shepherd,
I could bring a lamb,
If I were a Wise man
I could play my part,
Yet what I have I give Him,
Give my heart.

From 'In the bleak mid-winter'

'BEFORE THE PALING OF THE STARS'

Before the paling of the stars,
    Before the winter morn,
Before the earliest cock crow,
    Jesus Christ was born:
Born in a stable,
    Cradled in a manger,
In the world His hands had made
    Born a stranger.

From 'A Christmas Carol'

CHRISTMAS SONG

JOHN MORRISON

Softly, softly
Come to the manger and see Him.
Holy, holy
Peace He has come to restore.
Gently, gently
Mary His mother will hold Him.
Humbly, humbly
Shepherds and wise men adore.

'OH! HUSH THEE, OH! HUSH THEE, MY BABY SO SMALL'

E. J. FALCONER

Oh! hush Thee, oh! hush Thee, my Baby so small,
Dim is the light from the lamp on the wall,
Bright in the night sky shineth a star,
Leading the Kings who come from afar.

Oh! hush Thee, oh! hush Thee, my Baby so small,
Joseph is spreading the straw in the stall,
Soon wilt Thou sleep in the nook of my arm
Safe from all trouble and danger and harm.

From 'Cradle Song at Bethlehem'

58

SHEPHERDS REJOICE

Shepherds rejoice, your Saviour is nigh!
Sing o'er His cradle your sweet lullaby:
Lullaby, lullaby, lullaby sing;
Low in His cradle lies Jesus your King.

Mary her lovely babe lays to rest,
Folding his tender limbs close to her breast.
Lullaby, lullaby, lullaby sing;
Low in His cradle lies Jesus your King.

Joyful as all now homewards depart,
Cherish this scene of God's love in your heart;
Lullaby, lullaby, lullaby sing;
Low in His cradle lies Jesus your King.

French Carol

THE LORD JESUS

Unto us a child is born,
unto us a son is given.

Isaiah IX. 6

And Jesus grew tall and strong
and the grace of God was upon him.

St. Luke II. 52, Basic English

This is my commandment,
That ye love one another,
As I have loved you.

St. John XV. 12–13

'GENTLE JESUS, KING OF KINGS'

RODNEY BENNETT

Gentle Jesus, King of kings,
Yet the Lord of little things,
Though but small and young I be,
From Thy glory shine on me.

From 'Easter Parade'

'JESUS WENT TO CHURCH TO PRAY'

LILIAN MCCREA

Jesus went to Church to pray
Just as children do today,
Closed His eyes, and kneeling there,
Said like children everywhere—
'Father hold my hand and guide me,
Let me feel You close beside me,
Help me to understand Your ways
And bless me now and all my days'.

60

A CHILD'S MORNING PRAYER

J. KIRBY

Look down on me, a little one,
Whose life on earth is but begun:
Dear Saviour, smile on me.

Watch over me from day to day,
And when I work, or when I play,
Dear Saviour, smile on me.

Help me to do Thy holy will,
With lovely thoughts my mind to fill:
Dear Saviour, smile on me.

ALL OUR DAYS

ANONYMOUS

Lord of the loving heart,
May mine be loving too;
Lord of the gentle hands,
May mine be gentle too;
Lord of the willing feet,
May mine be willing too;
So may I grow more like to Thee
In all I say and do.

LOVING JESUS

CHARLES WESLEY

Loving Jesus, meek and mild,
Look upon a little child!

Make me gentle as Thou art,
Come and live within my heart.

Take my childish hand in Thine,
Guide these little feet of mine.

So shall all my happy days
Sing their pleasant song of praise;

And the world shall always see
Christ, the Holy Child, in me.

'HE WAS GREAT-HEARTED, TENDER, TRUE'

JOHN OXENHAM

He was great-hearted, tender, true,
And brave as any boy could be,
And very gentle, for He knew
That Love is God's own chivalry.

He was a boy—like you—and you—
As full of jokes, as full of fun,
But always He was bravely true,
And did no wrong to anyone.

From 'Gentlemen, The King!'

THE HOLY CHILD

G. STARR

The Holy Child went to and fro
In Mary's home of long ago,
And when His Mother called His name,
How quickly He rose up and came.
Lord Jesus in my home today,
I pray Thee help me to obey.

The Holy Child went to and fro
In Joseph's workshop long ago.
And, as He learnt, He understood
The way to make things strong and good.
Lord Jesus, when I work today,
Teach me to do it in Thy way.

'THE CHRIST-CHILD STOOD AT MARY'S KNEE'

G. K. CHESTERTON

The Christ-child stood at Mary's knee,
His hair was like a crown,
And all the flowers looked up at Him,
And all the stars looked down.

From 'A Christmas Carol'

'GOD BE IN MY HEAD'

ANONYMOUS

God be in my head
  And in my understanding;
God be in mine eyes
  And in my looking;
God be in my mouth
  And in my speaking;
God be in my heart
  And in my thinking.

From 'The Knight's Prayer'

SCHOOL

THIS IS OUR SCHOOL

This is our school.
May all here live happily together.
May our school be full of joy.
May love dwell here among us every day:
Love of one another,
Love of all people everywhere,
Love of life itself,
And love of God.
Let us remember
That as many hands build a house
So every child can make this school
A lovely place.

From 'The School Creed' of a school in Canada
(Paraphrase)

HOME

Verse

I remember, I remember,
The house where I was born,
The little window where the sun
Came peeping in at morn.

Thomas Hood

'GOD SEND US A LITTLE HOME'

FLORENCE BONE

God send us a little home,
To come back to, when we roam.

Red firelight and deep chairs,
Small white beds upstairs . . .

One picture on each wall,
Not many things at all.

God send us a little ground,
Tall trees standing round . . .

God bless, when winds blow,
Our little home and all we know.

From 'A Prayer for a little home'

WE THANK THEE, LOVING FATHER

ANONYMOUS

We thank Thee, loving Father,
For all Thy tender care,
For food and clothes and shelter,
And all the world so fair.

HOME

LEONARD CLARK

Snow in the air tonight,
Roads freeze:
No birds sing, cold trees,
But the kitchen is warm, bright.

BEST OF ALL

J. M. WESTRUP

I've got a lovely home,
With every single thing—
A mother and a father,
And a front-door bell to ring.
A dining-room and kitchen,
Some bedrooms and a hall,
But the baby in the cradle
Is the nicest thing of all.

PEOPLE WHO WORK FOR US

'WHEN HE HOLDS UP HIS HAND'

CLIVE SANSOM

When he holds up his hand,
All the traffic has to stand.
Every car, every bus,
Has to stop without a fuss.
They must wait in a row
Till the policeman tells them, 'Go!'

From 'The Policeman'

POST-MAN'S KNOCK

RODNEY BENNETT

Rattat! Rattat!
   There's the postman at the door,
He always knocks like that,
   No matter who it's for.
It may be a letter
   And it might be a box,
So I'm always very glad
   When the postman knocks.

Rattat! Rattat!
   Shall I run along to see
If he is on the mat
   With something meant for me?
It may be just a postcard,
   But it might be a box,
So I always run to look
   When the postman knocks.

67

'THERE ARE SO MANY THINGS TO DO TODAY'

MARY OSBORN

There are so many things to do today
  In city, field and street,
And people are going everywhere,
  With quickly hurrying feet.

Some are ploughing and sowing the seed,
  And some are reaping the grain;
And some, who worked the whole night through,
  Are coming home again.

And everywhere they come and go
  In sun and rain and sleet,
That we may have warm clothes to wear,
  And food enough to eat.

From 'Every Day'

I AM WONDERFULLY MADE

Verse

I will praise Thee; for I am wonderfully made.
Psalm CXXXIX. 14

'FOR ALL SKILLED HANDS, BOTH DELICATE AND STRONG'

J. D.

For all skilled hands, both delicate and strong—
Doctors' and nurses', soothing in their touch;
Sensitive artist-hands . . .
            . . . homely mother-hands
Busy with countless differing tasks each day;
For miners' hands that labour for our sakes;
For all hands rough and hard with honest work . . .
For these we thank Thee, Lord.
From 'A Thanksgiving'

'THOU WHOSE HANDS'

Thou, whose hands were skilled and strong,
Doing good work all day long,
Make our two hands kind and true,
Show us work that we can do.
Source unknown

PLAYTIME

Verse

What is this life if, full of care,
We have no time to stand and stare?

W. H. Davies

GO OUT

EILEEN MATHIAS

Go out
When the wind's about;
Let him buffet you
Inside out.

Go out
In a rainy drizzle;
Never sit by the fire
To sizzle.

Go out
When the snowflakes play;
Toss them about
On the white highway.

Go out
And stay till night;
When the sun is shedding
Its golden light.

THE SWING

ROBERT LOUIS STEVENSON

How would you like to go up in a swing,
    Up in the air so blue?
Oh, I do think it the pleasantest thing
    Ever a child can do!

Up in the air and over the wall,
    Till I can see so wide,
Rivers and trees and cattle and all
    Over the countryside.

Till I look down on the garden green
    Down on the roof so brown—
Up in the air I go flying again,
    Up in the air and down.

SKIPPING

HILDA ROSTRON

Over my head and under my toes
Watch the way my skipping rope goes.
Over my head, ten toes off the ground,
See my rope swing round and round.
I can skip slowly, I can skip fast:
Watch my rope go whirling past.
Over my head and under my toes
It's fun the way my skipping rope goes.

THE WOOD OF FLOWERS

JAMES STEPHENS

I went to the Wood of Flowers,
No one went with me;
I was there alone for hours;
I was happy as could be,
In the Wood of Flowers!

There was grass
On the ground;
There were leaves
On the tree;

And the wind
Had a sound
Of such sheer
Gaiety,

That I
Was as happy
As happy could be,
In the Wood of Flowers!

'THERE ISN'T TIME'

ELEANOR FARJEON

There isn't time, there isn't time
    To do the things I want to do—
With all the mountain tops to climb
And all the woods to wander through.
And all the seas to sail upon,
And everywhere there is to go,
And all the people, everywhere,
Who live upon the earth to know.

'THROUGH THE SUNNY HOURS I PLAY'

JAMES STEPHENS

Through the sunny hours I play
    Where the stream is wandering,
Plucking daisies by the way;
    And I laugh and dance and sing,
While the birds fly here and there
Singing on the sunny air.

From 'Day and Night'

'BRING THE HOOP, AND BRING THE BALL'

Bring the hoop, and bring the ball,
Come with happy faces all;
Let us make a merry ring,
Talk and laugh and dance and sing.
Quickly, quickly, come away,
For it is a pleasant day.

From 'It is a pleasant day'

INDEX OF FIRST LINES

74

INDEX OF SUBJECTS

Numbers refer to pages

ACKNOWLEDGEMENTS

The author and publisher are grateful to the following for permission to reproduce copyright material from the sources shown:

An extract from 'A Piper' by Seumas O'Sullivan from *Verses Sacred and Profane*, T. Fisher Unwin, 1908.

A. & C. Black Ltd for the extract from 'The Policeman' from *Rhythm Rhymes* by Clive Samson, ed. by Ruth Samson.

Blackie & Sons Ltd for 'Promise' by Florence Lacey from *In Poem-Town*, Book 3.

Blandford Press Ltd for the extract from 'Harvest Time' by D. M. Prescott from *The Infant Teacher's Assembly Book*.

Mrs H. M. Davies & Jonathan Cape Ltd for extracts from 'My Garden' and 'Winter's Beauty' from *The Complete Poems of W. H. Davies*.

The Executors of the James Joyce Estate & Jonathan Cape Ltd for 'Goldenhair' from *Chamber Music* by James Joyce.

Christine Chaundler for the extract from 'There's A Tree Out In Our Garden'.

Curtis Brown Ltd for 'We thank you, Lord of Heaven' and 'For Swift and Gallant Horses' by Jan Struther.

J. M. Dent & Sons Ltd & Miss D. E. Collins for the extract from 'The Christchild stood at Mary's knee' by G. K. Chesterton.

Olive Enoch for the extract from 'Bluebells'.

Mrs Doris M. Gill for the extract from 'Come, Let Us Remember the Joys Of the Town'.

Harper & Row Ltd for the extract from 'God Send Us A Little Home' by Florence Bone.

Leonard Clark & Rupert Hart-Davis Ltd, for 'Sparrow'.

William Heinemann Ltd for 'Prayer for Gentleness to all Creatures' from *Collected Poems* by John Galsworthy, and 'My New Year's Wish Shall Be' from *The Collected Poems of Edmund Gosse*.

James Reeves & William Heinemann Ltd for 'Beech Leaves' from *The Wandering Moon*.

Eleanor Farjeon & David Higham Associates Ltd for 'There Are Big Waves' from *The Children's Bells*, Oxford University Press; 'Window Boxes' and 'The Garden Flowers Inside The Wall', published by Michael Joseph Ltd; and 'The Fruit Hangs Ripe' and 'There Isn't Time'.

Mrs Iris Wise & Macmillan & Co Ltd for 'Blue Stars and Gold', 'The Wood of Flowers', 'White Fields' and 'Donnybrook' from *Collected Poems* by James Stephens, and 'Day and Night', and 'This way to Winter'.

Michael Gibson & Macmillan & Co Ltd for 'Michael's Song' from *Collected Poems 1905–1925* by Wilfred Gibson.

The Trustees of The Hardy Estate and Macmillan & Co Ltd for 'Weathers' from *Collected Poems of Thomas Hardy*.

Mrs Shanks & Macmillan & Co Ltd for the extract from 'The Storm' from *Poems 1912–1932* by Edward Shanks.

The National Society for 'The Holy Child' by G. Starr.

James Reeves & Oxford University Press for the extract 'Time to go Home' from *The Blackbird in the Lilac*.

The Clarendon Press for the extracts from 'First Spring Morning' and 'The Cliff-Top' by Robert Bridges; 'Great Lord and King of Earth' by Jessie Pope; and the extract from 'A Rhyme of the Harvest' by Lucy Diamond from *One Hundred Poems for Children*.

Religious Education Press for the extracts from 'Sing Praises' by J. M. MacDougall Ferguson.

Sidgwick & Jackson Ltd for the extract from 'Blackbird' from *The Collected Poems Of John Drinkwater*.

The Society of Authors & Jonathan Cape Ltd for the extract from 'Loveliest of Trees' by A. E. Housman.

The Society of Authors for the extract from 'The Beech Tree' by Rose Fyleman.

Nancy Byrd Turner for 'Water' and 'God gives so Many Lovely Things' from *God's Providence*.

Miss Ann Wolfe for 'The Blackbird' from *Kensington Gardens* by Humbert Wolfe.

Michael Yeats & Macmillan & Co Ltd for 'To A Squirrel At Kyle-Na-No' from the *Collected Poems of W. B. Yeats*.

Mrs Joan Bennett for 'My dog, Spot', 'Merry Birds', 'Gentle Jesus, King of Kings' and 'Postman's Knock' by Rodney Bennett.

S.P.C.K. for the extract from 'Every Day' from *Good and Gay* by Mary Osborn.

Lilian McCrea for 'The Doormouse'.

Evans Brothers Ltd for 'I Love All Shining Things' and 'For Joy of Glowing Colour' by E. Gould; 'Poppies' by P. A. Ropes; 'Welcome to Spring' by Irene Thompson; 'The World is Full of Colour' by A. White; 'Mr Squirrel' by V. M. Julian; 'June' by I. F. Pawsey; 'The Sea' by E. M. Adams; 'Leaf Fall' by E. H. Ray; 'Go Out' by E. Matthias; 'Skipping', 'As Soft as Feathers' and 'Seeds' by Hilda Rostron; 'Song of the Wise Men' by N. Bettesworth; 'A Child's Morning Prayer' by J. Kirby.

P. R. Chalmers Trust and Methuen & Co Ltd for 'I Like the Rain' by Patrick Chalmers.